King Arthur

re-told by
Philip Page

Published in association with
The Basic Skills Agency

Hodder &
A MEMBER OF THE HO

Acknowledgements
Cover: Doug Lewis
Illustrations: Philip Page

Orders; please contact Bookpoint Ltd, 39 Milton Park, Abingdon, Oxon OX14
4TD. Telephone: (44) 01235 400414, Fax: (44) 01235 400454. Lines are open
from 9.00–6.00, Monday to Saturday, with a 24 hour message answering service.
Email address: orders@bookpoint.co.uk

British Library Cataloguing in Publication Data
A catalogue record for this title is available from the British Library

ISBN 0 340 77678 1

First published 2000
Impression number 10 9 8 7 6 5 4 3 2 1
Year   2005 2004 2003 2002 2001 2000

Copyright © 2000 Philip Page

Typeset by GreenGate Publishing Services, Tonbridge, Kent.
Printed in Great Britain for Hodder and Stoughton Educational, a division of
Hodder Headline Plc, 338 Euston Road, London NW1 3BH, by Atheneum
Press, Gateshead, Tyne & Wear

King Arthur

Contents

About the story

The People

○ Arthur, King of Britain
○ Uther, Arthur' father
○ Igraine, Arthur's mother
○ Guinevere, Arthur's wife
○ Merlin, a wizard who helps Arthur
○ Lancelot, Arthur's bravest knight
  and best friend
● Morgana, Arthur's half-sister
○ Mordred, Morgana's son

How to say the names

Uther – Ooth-er
Igraine – Ee-grain
Morgana – Moo-gar-na
Excalibur – Ex-kal-ee-ber
Bedivere – Bed-ee-veer
Lancelot – Lans-ee-lot
Guinevere – Gwin-ee-veer
Mordred – Moor-dred

1

Merlin

Many, many years ago there lived in Britain
a wizard called Merlin.

It was said that his mother had been human
but that his father was a demon.

Most people were afraid of Merlin.
They did not trust him.
They were afraid of the magic spells
he could cast.

At that time Britain did not have
a single king.
There were many kings and warlords.
They were always fighting each other.

One of the most powerful of them
was Uther Pendragon.

Uther fell in love
with the Duke of Cornwall's wife.
Her name was Igraine.
She was the most beautiful woman in Britain.

Uther attacked the Duke's castle.
Time after time his soldiers were driven back.

Uther did not know what to do.
Then he had an idea.
He sent for Merlin to help him with his magic.

Merlin listened to Uther.
Then he spoke.

'Tonight you must give orders
for your army to leave.
The Duke will think you have given up
and chase you.
I will cast a spell on Igraine.
She will think you are her husband
and you can spend the night with her.'

Uther was pleased and started to give orders
for his soldiers to leave.

'Wait,' said Merlin.
'There is a price to pay for my magic.'

'Ask it,' said Uther,
'I will pay you anything.'

'Igraine will give birth to a son,'
said Merlin. 'He will be your child.
As soon as he is born,
you must give him to me.'

Uther agreed to what Merlin had said.

That night Merlin cast his spell.
Igraine thought that Uther was her husband.
Her young daughter, however, was not fooled.
Her name was Morgana.

That same night the Duke was killed.

Uther later married Igraine.
When she gave birth to a son,
Merlin came for him.

'His name will be Arthur,' said Merlin.
'When he grows up,
he will become a great king.'

Morgana heard what Merlin said.
She hated her half-brother, Arthur.
She swore that she would destroy him.

2

The Sword in
the Stone

Uther became the most powerful king
in Britain.
When he died many men wanted to become
the next king.

Merlin said that they should all meet
in London on Christmas Day.
He told them the true king
would be chosen then.

On Christmas Day a stone appeared
in a London churchyard.
In the stone was a blacksmith's anvil.
Fixed in the anvil was a sword.

Words were carved in the stone.
They said that whoever could pull out the sword
was the rightful King of Britain.

News of the sword in the stone spread quickly.
People came to London from all over Britain.

They all tried to pull out the sword.
Not one of them could move it!

Among them was a knight called
Sir Ector and his son, Kay.
Merlin had given Arthur to Ector.
He was brought up as Kay's brother.
Merlin had not told Ector who Arthur was.

A great tournament was held.
Kay was keen to take part
but he had left his sword at the house
where they were staying.

Arthur went to fetch it.
He found that the house was locked up.
Everybody had gone to the tournament.

He knew Kay would be angry with him –
but what could he do?

Then he remembered somebody saying
that there was a sword in a stone
in the churchyard.

He ran there, took hold of the sword
and pulled.
It slid out easily!

Sir Ector and the other knights knew
which sword it was as soon as they saw it.
They did not believe Arthur when he told them
he had pulled it out.

They all went back to the church.
Arthur pushed the sword back in the stone.
Once again all the knights
tried to pull it out.
Once again they all failed.
Then Arthur walked up to the stone.
He pulled the sword out easily.

Almost at once Merlin appeared.
'This is Arthur,' he told them all.
'He is Uther's son.
He is the rightful king of all Britain!'

One by one, most of the knights
agreed to serve Arthur.
A few did not.
They were angry and said they would bring
armies to fight against Arthur.

3

Excalibur

Arthur had to fight many battles
before everybody in Britain
agreed he was the true king.

In one of these battles he broke his sword.

'Come with me, ' said Merlin.
'I know where there is another sword.'

He took Arthur to the side of a large lake.
A grey mist covered the water.

The mist slid away and Arthur saw
an amazing sight.
An arm, clothed in white silk, rose up
out of the water.
Its hand held a sword!

Arthur found a small boat and rowed out
to take the sword.

'This sword is called Excalibur,'
Merlin told him.
'It belongs to the Lady of the Lake.
When you fight with it you will
never be defeated.
When you wear its sheath you will
never be wounded.'

He told Arthur he must never give the sword
to anybody else.

'When you have no further use for it,'
Merlin said, 'you must return it
to the Lady of the Lake.'

4

The Round Table

Arthur built a great castle.
It had tall towers and strong walls.
He called it Camelot.

In a great hall in the castle
there was a huge round table.
There were seats at the table for all
the greatest knights in the land.

One by one the knights took their places.
Their names were carved on the seats.
Among them were Sir Bedivere and Sir Kay.
Then the greatest knight of all
took his place at the table.
His name was Sir Lancelot.

When they were all gathered there,
Arthur spoke to them.

'When we sit here,' he said,
'we are all equal.
Nobody is more important
than the person who sits next to him.'

Arthur made all the knights promise
never to fight each other.
They should fight against evil instead.

'Together we can bring peace to this country,'
Arthur said.
'We must help the poor and the weak.
We must fight for what is right
and against what is wrong.'

Then he drew his sword Excalibur.
He held it up high.
The light flashed on its gleaming blade.

'All those who agree, may join the company
of the Knights of the Round Table,' he said.

The knights all drew their swords too.
'We agree,' they cried.
'Long live King Arthur and the
Knights of the Round Table!'

5

Guinevere

One day, Arthur was talking to Merlin.
'It is time for me to get married,' he said.
'Have you seen the woman you want to marry?
Merlin asked.

'Yes,' Arthur said. 'Her name is Guinevere.'

For a moment Merlin looked sad and troubled.
'That is not a wise choice,' he said slowly.

'Why not?' Arthur asked.
'The country is at peace now
and I must look to the future.
I want a son to be king when I am gone.'

'What is the matter with Guinevere?' he added.

'She is beautiful and she will
always love you,' said the wizard,
'but she will bring you great sorrow.'

'I don't see how,' said Arthur,
'if she always loves me.'

Merlin turned to go.
Arthur called after him.
'If you can see the future, Merlin,
can you tell me if I will have a son?'

Merlin did not look back at Arthur.
'Oh yes,' he said. 'You will have a son.'

Arthur sent messages to Guinevere's father.
He agreed to the marriage.
Guinevere was very excited
at the thought of marrying the king.

Arthur sent his best friend and bravest
knight to bring Guinevere to Camelot.
That was Lancelot.

As soon as Lancelot saw Guinevere
he fell in love with her.
He thought that she was in love with him too –
but he said nothing of his feelings.

Arthur and Guinevere were married.
There was a great feast at Camelot.
There was music and dancing
and a tournament.

Lancelot won the tournament but everybody
noticed that he seemed unhappy.
He would not tell anybody why he was sad.
He could not tell them that he loved the wife
of his best friend, the King.

There were two people who knew
about his secret.
One was Merlin.
The other was Arthur's half-sister – Morgana.
Like Merlin, she too had magic powers.

6

Morgana

For years and years Morgana waited.
She never forgot how her mother had been
tricked by Merlin's spell.

She wanted to destroy Arthur and the
Knights of the Round Table in revenge.
Luckily her magic was not as strong
as Merlin's.
Merlin protected Arthur and all at Camelot.

Then her chance came!

Merlin told Arthur that he was going away.
'If you are wise and watchful,' Merlin told
Arthur, 'you will no longer need me.'

'Before you leave, tell me what dangers
are ahead,' said Arthur.

'Beware of those close to you,' said Merlin.

Morgana began to make her plans.
First she stole Excalibur's sheath.
Now Arthur could be wounded.

Then she began to spread stories about
Lancelot and Guinevere.

Finally she used Merlin's spell to make
Arthur think that she was Guinevere.
She slept with Arthur and later
gave birth to a son. She called him Mordred.

'You will destroy Arthur for me,'
she whispered to the newborn baby.

7

The Holy Grail

One day Arthur and all his knights
were seated at the Round Table.
Suddenly the sound of thunder filled the air.
A bright beam of light shone in the room.

The knights were amazed and afraid.
What they then saw filled them with wonder!

A cup appeared, covered in a white silk cloth.
Nobody could see who carried it.
Then, as suddenly as it appeared, it vanished.

'That was the Holy Grail,' said Sir Gawaine.
'It is the cup Jesus Christ drank from.
I will go to try to find it and see it again.'

All the other knights agreed to go too.
They would search for the Grail for a year.

Arthur was sad.
He knew that many of his knights
might never return.
He was afraid that this was the end
of the Knights of the Round Table.

The knights who went in search of the Grail
had many adventures. Some were killed.
Most never found the Grail.
Only a pure knight who had no faults
could see it again.

Three knights did find the Grail.
Their names were Sir Galahad, Sir Percivale
and Sir Bors.
Only Bors lived to return to Camelot.

8

Lancelot and Guinevere

When Mordred grew up he, too, became
a Knight of the Round Table. Like his mother
he wanted to cause trouble for Arthur.

He soon saw how he could do this.

Most people at Camelot knew that Lancelot
and Guinevere loved each other.
Perhaps even Arthur knew it –
but nobody talked about it.

Mordred knew that Guinevere
still loved Arthur.
He also knew that Lancelot
was still Arthur's best friend.
Mordred wanted to prove that they were lovers.

One night a servant told him that Lancelot
and Guinevere were alone together.
Mordred and thirteen other knights
broke into their room.

There was a fierce fight. Lancelot killed
all the knights and wounded Mordred.
Then he escaped and left Camelot.

King Arthur was forced to put Guinevere
on trial.
She was found guilty.
Her punishment was to be burned to death.

The day of her execution came.
She was tied to a wooden stake.

Just before the fire was lit,
she spoke to Arthur.

'I have always loved you,' she said.
'I am sorry that I loved Lancelot too.'

Just then a knight in full armour
galloped into the crowd.
It was Lancelot!
He fought his way through Arthur's soldiers
and rescued Guinevere.
He took her back to his own castle.

Lancelot never returned to Camelot.
Guinevere later became a nun.

Mordred and Morgana had succeeded!
Arthur had lost his queen
and his best friend and bravest knight.

Mordred gathered a great army.
He sent word to Arthur to meet him in battle.
The fight would decide who would be the king.

9

Avalon

The armies of Arthur and Mordred
faced each other.
All the soldiers were nervous.
Arthur rode out to meet Mordred.
He wanted to try to make peace.

Just then a snake bit a soldier's ankle.
He drew his sword to kill it.
Both armies thought that was the sign
to attack.
The battle began.

The Battle of Camlan lasted all day.
By evening Mordred was dead.
His army had been defeated.

Arthur, too, was badly wounded.
He knew he was dying.

He called Sir Bedivere to him.
'Take Excalibur,' he told Bedivere,
'and throw it into that lake nearby.'

Bedivere took the great sword to the lake –
but he did not throw it in.

'What did you see?' Arthur asked him
when he came back.

'I saw the ripples on the lake – nothing else.'

'Go back and do as I have told you,'
Arthur told him.

This time Bedivere threw Excalibur far out
into the lake.
Before it hit the surface, the Lady of the Lake
reached up and caught it.

Just as the sun was about to set a boat came
to the shore beside the battlefield.
On board were queens with gold crowns and
ladies dressed in black.

'They have come for me,' said Arthur.
'They will take me to the enchanted land
of Avalon.'

The boat sailed slowly away.
Arthur was never seen again.

Some say that he is not dead but sleeping.
When Britain needs him, he and his knights
will wake and come to its rescue.

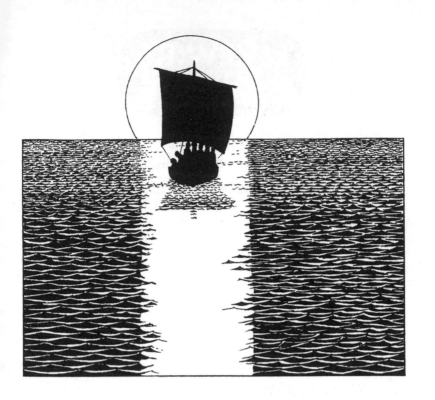

LIVEWIRE
MYTHS AND
LEGENDS

If you have enjoyed reading this book, you may be interested in other titles in the *Livewire* series.

King Oedipus
Medea
Hercules
Jason and the Golden Fleece
Rama and Sita
The Wooden Horse of Troy
Beowulf
The Odyssey
Robin Hood